Literacy BASICS

FOR AGES 8-9 KEY STAGE 2

Contents

Verbs

Look and learn

The boy **kicked** the ball.

Many verbs are **doing** words. They describe **actions**.

The boy **is** muddy.

Some verbs are **being** words.

Practice

Choose the best verb to complete each sentence.

are	yapped	invented	jumped	dug
left	dried	picked	learn	is

1. The professor _____ a strange machine.
2. Shireen _____ her hair with a towel.
3. We _____ how to spell at school.
4. Tadpoles _____ baby frogs.
5. In the summer it _____ hot.
6. The toad _____ out of the pond.
7. The man _____ in a hurry.
8. I _____ up the letters off the mat.
9. The lady _____ her garden.
10. The little dog _____ all day.

Challenge

The verbs in the sentences below are mixed up. Correct each verb.

1. A footballer ploughs. ___kicks___
2. A clown chops. _____
3. A lumberjack bakes. _____
4. A builder jokes. _____
5. A shop assistant climbs. _____
6. A cook saws. _____
7. A teacher hammers. _____
8. A mountaineer kicks. _____
9. A carpenter prays. _____
10. A priest sews. _____
11. A tailor sells. _____
12. A farmer teaches. _____

Phonemes

Look and learn

A **phoneme** is the **smallest unit of sound** in a word.

A phoneme may be made up of **one or more letters** which make **one sound**.

The g**ir**l had c**ur**ly hair.

Practice

Choose the correct phoneme to complete each word.

1. ee ea s_ea_t	**2.** ai ay holid_____	**3.** ow oa wind_____	**4.** oo ow thr_____
5. u oo p_____sh	**6.** oy oi p_____nt	**7.** ow ou h_____l	**8.** aw au cl_____
9. au or s_____cer	**10.** ou ow l_____d	**11.** ew oo f_____d	**12.** oi oy enj_____

Challenge

Think of three words containing the following phonemes:

1. ir (as in b**ir**d)　　_____　_____　_____

2. are (as in sc**are**)　_____　_____　_____

3. ea (as in br**ea**d)　_____　_____　_____

4. ur (as in f**ur**)　_____　_____　_____

5. ere (as in th**ere**)　_____　_____　_____

6. y (as in fl**y**)　_____　_____　_____

7. air (as in f**air**)　_____　_____　_____

3

Verb tenses

Look and learn

Verbs can be written in different **tenses**.

Yesterday I **swam** in the sea.

Now I **am swimming** in the pool.

Tomorrow I **will swim** in the river.

| This happened in the **past**. The verb is in the **past tense**. | This is happening **now**. The verb is in the **present tense**. | This will happen in the **future**. The verb is in the **future tense**. |

Practice

Underline the verb in each sentence. Decide which tense it is in.

	past	present	future
1. I will go to bed early tonight.			✓
2. We drank all the lemonade.			
3. Alex is riding his bicycle.			
4. They crossed the busy street.			
5. Next week we will go on holiday.			
6. The car broke down.			
7. We gave the dog a bone.			
8. I will sleep in the tent in the summer.			
9. I am eating my dinner.			
10. Glen likes his sandwiches.			

Challenge

Write these sentences in the future tense.

1. I got up at six o'clock.   _I will get up at six o'clock._
2. I played with my friend.   _____
3. We rode our bikes to school.   _____
4. In the morning we did Maths.   _____
5. For lunch I had pizza.   _____
6. In the afternoon I painted a picture.   _____
7. I went to the shop after school.   _____
8. In the evening I watched TV.   _____

Syllables

Look and learn

When we say words slowly, we can hear how they may be broken down into **smaller parts** called **syllables**. Each syllable must contain at least **one vowel**.

gar – den

sun – shine

These words are both made of **two** syllables.

Practice

Add the syllables. Write the words you make.

1. den + tist = _____dentist_____

2. win + dow = _____

3. mag + net = _____

4. un + lock = _____

5. in + side = _____

6. sis + ter = _____

7. spi + der = _____

8. ti + ger = _____

9. ro + bot = _____

10. la + bel = _____

11. he + ro = _____

12. pu + pil = _____

Challenge

Join up the first and second syllable of each word.

1. pen   tern   _____

2. lan   nap   _____

3. trum   dent   _____

4. in   cils ⟶ _____pencils_____

5. kid   tor   _____

6. si   vent   _____

7. stu   cess   _____

8. tea   pet   _____

9. doc   cher   _____

10. prin   lent   _____

Suffixes

Look and learn

A **suffix** is a **group of letters** we add to the **end of a word**.
A suffix changes the **meaning** of the word or the **job the word does**.

build ⟶ build**er**
(verb)　　　　　　　　　　　　　　　(noun)

Practice

What do we call someone who:

1. paints?　_____a painter_____
2. sings?　_____
3. bakes?　_____
4. gardens?　_____
5. boxes?　_____
6. skates?　_____
7. reports?　_____
8. cleans?　_____
9. dances?　_____
10. drums?　_____
11. drives?　_____
12. swims?　_____

Challenge

Make these verbs into **er** or **or** nouns by adding the correct suffix.

1. trade　_____trader_____
2. act　_____
3. inspect　_____
4 print　_____
5. vote　_____
6. visit　_____
7. profess　_____
8. edit　_____
9. glide　_____
10. sail　_____

Alphabetical order

Look and learn

Many reference books are organised in **alphabetical order**.

 paper   pavement   paw    beat   bean   bear

These words are arranged in alphabetical order according to their **third** letter.

These words are arranged in alphabetical order according to their **fourth** letter.

Practice

Arrange these words according to their third letter.

1. slip   slap   sleep   _____

2. flick   flame   flock   _____

3. prod   pray   prepare   _____

4. shoulder sharp   shut   _____

5. drag   drum   drop   dry   _____

6. beg   bee   beak   bell   _____

7. cork   cost   coat   code   _____

8. cheese   chip   chatter   chop   _____

9. badge   base   baby   balloon _____

10. pet   pest   pear   pebble   _____

Challenge

Think of a different letter to complete each word.
Then write the words in alphabetical order.

1. bea___t   bea___er   bea___en   _____

2. can___le   can___l   can___on   _____

3. com___uter   com___c   com___and   _____

4. hel___ing   hel___o   hel___copter _____

5. scr___p   scr___b   scr___ll   _____

6. str___ke   str___ngth   str___de   _____

Homophones

Look and learn

Homophones are words that **sound alike** but have **different spellings** and **different meanings**.

Ben **rode** along the **road** on his bike.

Practice

Join up the pairs of homophones.

ball	heard	bare	here	faint	their	find	fir

berth	hair	draft	check	flour	tide	steal

hare	draught	birth	tied	fur	steel	cheque

bear	fined	flower	there	herd	feint	bawl	hear

Challenge

Underline the words that are incorrectly spelled. Write the sentences correctly.

Last weak I thought I wood go for a sale on the see. I went down to the key, and maid my weigh to the boat. The tied was write inn.

_____

_____

_____

_____

Adverbs

Look and learn

Adverbs tell us **more about verbs**. Many adverbs tell us **how** something happened. Many adverbs end in **ly**.

The children are laughing **happily**.

Practice

Underline the verb and circle the adverb in each sentence.

1. The tortoise moved slowly.
2. Rain fell heavily.
3. Tom spoke rudely to his mother.
4. Shahla smiled sweetly.
5. The old man smacked his lips noisily.
6. Cross the road carefully.
7. I wrote my story neatly.
8. Angrily I kicked the ball away.
9. The lion growled fiercely.
10. In the sky the sun shone brightly.

Challenge

Match the adverbs with similar meanings.

1. wearily	timidly
2. bravely	clearly
3. shyly	sluggishly
4. happily	boisterously
5. distinctly	tiredly
6. sadly	cautiously
7. badly	unhappily
8. slowly	cheerfully
9. noisily	fearlessly
10. carefully	poorly

Words within words

Look and learn

Look for **small words** within **longer words** to help you spell them.

I won the Lottery last week!

Never be**lie**ve **lie**s.

Practice

| friend | every | want | heard | brother |
| island | breakfast | hospital | separate | business |

Which word contains:

1. land? _____

2. bus? _____

3. end? _____

4. rat? _____

5. broth? _____

6. ear? _____

7. spit? _____

8. very? _____

9. ant? _____

10. break? _____

Challenge

Find and write the ten long words in this puzzle. Underline a small word in each.

a	b	c	o	u	n	t	r	y	d	e	f
k	n	o	w	l	e	d	g	e	h	i	j
m	r	s	l	i	g	h	t	n	i	n	g
t	p	r	e	s	e	n	t	u	v	w	x
y	z	s	a	n	d	w	i	c	h	a	b
c	d	e	f	g	h	i	s	w	o	r	d
j	k	l	v	e	g	e	t	a	b	l	e
m	w	e	a	t	h	e	r	n	o	p	z
r	s	t	v	w	e	i	g	h	t	x	y
z	a	w	h	o	l	e	b	c	d	e	f

1. _____country_____

2. _____

3. _____

4. _____

5. _____

6. _____

7. _____

8. _____

9. _____

10. _____

Adverbs again

Look and learn

clever – cleverly

We can just add **ly** to many root words.

happy – happily

If the word ends in **y**, we change the **y** to **i** and add **ly**.

gentle – gently

If the word ends in **e**, we drop the **e** and add **ly**.

Practice

Change these adjectives to adverbs.

	adjectives	adverbs
1.	glad	gladly
2.	slow	
3.	proud	
4.	hungry	
5.	lazy	
6.	merry	
7.	easy	
8.	simple	
9.	humble	
10.	horrible	

Challenge

Write the adjective from which each of these adverbs was made.

1. willingly ___willing___   **2.** gratefully _____   **3.** wearily _____

4. idly _____   **5.** miserably _____   **6.** skilfully _____

7. bravely _____   **8.** steadily _____   **9.** luckily _____

10. noisily _____   **11.** suddenly _____   **12.** truly _____

Adjectives

Look and learn

An **adjective** is a **describing** word. It gives us more information about a **noun**.

The **brave** knight fought the **ugly** troll.

Practice

Choose the best adjective from the ladder to complete each sentence.

heavy
sad
nasty
choppy
sour
loud
howling
blunt
slippery
muddy

1. The lemon tasted very _____sour_____.

2. When it rained the ground became _____.

3. The case was too _____ to lift.

4. The knife was very _____.

5. There was a _____ smell coming from the dustbin.

6. The _____ eel got away.

7. The _____ ending of the film made me cry.

8. The referee blew a _____ blast on his whistle.

9. The _____ sea made me feel sick.

10. The _____ wind blew some trees down.

Challenge

Write a suitable adjective to go with each noun.

1. a _____ princess	**2.** a _____ giant	**3.** a _____ cave
4. a _____ cat	**5.** a _____ fire	**6.** a _____ owl
7. a _____ tree	**8.** a _____ monster	**9.** a _____ sheep
10. a _____ wood	**11.** a _____ cottage	**12.** a _____ necklace

Similes

Look and learn

A **simile** is when one thing is **compared** with another.

as busy as a bee

as slippery as a fish

Practice

Choose the best adjective from the wall to complete each simile.

soft	cool	flat	sweet
heavy	cold	red	slow
smooth	strong	light	gentle

1. as ____cold____ as ice

2. as _____ as honey

3. as _____ as silk

4. as _____ as a feather

5. as _____ as butter

6. as _____ as a pancake

7. as _____ as a dove

8. as _____ as a beetroot

9. as _____ as a cucumber

10. as _____ as iron

11. as _____ as a tortoise

12. as _____ as an ox

Challenge

Write a suitable noun to complete each simile.

1. as wise as an ____owl____

2. as fierce as a _____

3. as tall as a _____

4. as sharp as a _____

5. as hot as a _____

6. as old as a _____

7. as straight as a _____

8. as playful as a _____

9. as dry as a _____

10. as thin as a _____

11. as sour as _____

12. as rich as a _____

Common word endings

Look and learn

Look for **common letter patterns** to help you learn your spellings.

fl**are**

sc**are**

st**are**

Practice

Make and write these words.

f
m
n → ight
r
s

1. _fight_
2. _____
3. _____
4. _____
5. _____

fu
ba
do → dge
bri
he

6. _____
7. _____
8. _____
9. _____
10. _____

m
c
b → ore
s
t

11. _____
12. _____
13. _____
14. _____
15. _____

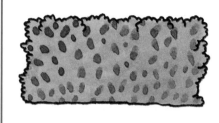

Challenge

Choose the correct ending from the box to complete each word.

1. sh<u>ould</u>

2. govern_____

3. sta_____

4. en_____

5. cl_____

6. bl_____

7. sp_____

8. ins_____

9. ca_____

10. appear_____

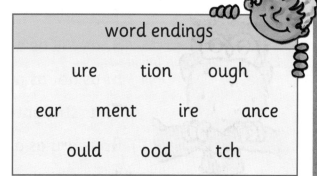

word endings			
ure	tion	ough	
ear	ment	ire	ance
ould	ood	tch	

Comparing adjectives

Look and learn

Emma is **strong**.

Amy is **stronger**.

Shireen is the **strongest**.

When we **compare two nouns** we use a **comparative adjective**.

When we **compare three or more** nouns we use a **superlative adjective**.

Practice

Complete this chart.

	adjective	comparative adjective	superlative adjective
1.	light	lighter	
2.	fast		fastest
3.		rounder	
4.	soft		
5.			longest
6.		colder	
7.	smooth		
8.			slowest
9.		sharper	
10.	rough		

Challenge

Write the comparative and superlative form of each adjective. Take care with the spelling!

1. safe   safer   safest   **2.** large _____ _____

3. tame _____ _____   **4.** hot _____ _____

5. thin _____ _____   **6.** sad _____ _____

7. heavy _____ _____   **8.** lucky _____ _____

9. ugly _____ _____   **10.** pretty _____ _____

Look and learn

A **suffix** is a **group of letters** we add to the **end of a word**. A suffix changes the **meaning** of the word or the **job** that the word does.

music – music**al**

Practice

Find ten nouns in the wordsearch. Make them into adjectives by adding the suffix **al**.

a	b	c	m	u	s	i	c	d	e
c	o	m	i	c	f	g	h	j	k
l	m	o	r	s	m	a	g	i	c
t	u	p	e	r	s	o	n	v	w
x	y	z	a	c	o	a	s	t	h
a	c	c	i	d	e	n	t	g	i
d	f	s	e	a	s	o	n	h	j
k	l	m	n	o	r	i	g	i	n
o	p	t	o	p	i	c	q	r	s
m	e	c	h	a	n	i	c	t	u

1. _____music_____   _____musical_____
2. _____   _____
3. _____   _____
4. _____   _____
5. _____   _____
6. _____   _____
7. _____   _____
8. _____   _____
9. _____   _____
10. _____   _____

Challenge

Choose the correct suffix to finish each word.

1. | ment | tion |

argu__ment__

2. | ary | ic |

athlet_____

3. | ic | ary |

custom_____

4. | hood | ness |

ill_____

5. | ship | hood |

child_____

6. | ness | ship |

leader_____

7. | ate | en |

dark_____

8. | tion | ate |

punctu_____

9. | ify | ise |

horr_____

10. | en | ise |

magnet_____

Gender words

Look and learn

Nouns may be classified according to their **gender**.

 a girl

 a boy

 a teacher

| Nouns which refer to **females** are **feminine**. | Nouns which refer to **males** are **masculine**. | Nouns which refer to **either** male or female are **common**. |

Practice

Write each noun in the correct column in the chart.

queen   boy   uncle   girl   pupil   husband   friend   teacher
king   aunt   wife   doctor   child   niece   nephew

masculine	feminine	common
	queen	

Challenge

Write each sentence. Change every masculine noun into into a feminine noun.

1. My father was talking to my uncle. ___My mother was talking to my aunt.___

2. The king looked at the prince. _____

3. The man told his son off. _____

4. My brother is going to be a policeman. _____

5. Lord Jones spoke to Mr Derby. _____

Contractions

Look and learn

We sometimes **shorten** a word by **leaving out** some letters. We use an **apostrophe** to show where letters have been left out.

I've lost my pen.

Don't worry! I'll buy you a new one.

I've = I have   don't = do not   I'll = I will

Practice

Match up each short word with its longer form.

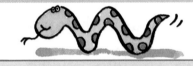

1. we're	can not		**7.** you're	we will
2. wasn't	it is		**8.** I'm	will not
3. can't	we are		**9.** we'll	you are
4. don't	did not		**10.** they've	she is
5. didn't	was not		**11.** won't	they have
6. it's	do not		**12.** she's	I am

Challenge

Write each sentence. Write a short word to replace the underlined words.

1. <u>It is</u> a horrible day.   It's a horrible day.

2. <u>You have</u> got a lovely hairstyle. _____

5. The dog <u>does not</u> have a lead. _____

4. <u>He is</u> cheating. _____

5. <u>We will</u> do it later. _____

6. I <u>did not</u> know what to do. _____

7. <u>They are</u> his shorts. _____

8. <u>I would</u> rather do it myself. _____

Commas

Look and learn

Pass it to me, Ben.

The game, a cup final, was nearly over.

Commas are used to separate **extra bits** that are **added** to sentences.

Commas help to **break up** longer sentences **into smaller parts**.

Practice

Put the missing commas in each of these sentences.

1. Put on your coat Emma.

2. Sorry miss.

3. We'll go now shall we?

4. No don't do that!

5. The rabbit a white fluffy animal escaped from its cage.

6. I saw two children Sam and Peter in the shop.

7. To my surprise the children did not recognise me.

8. One of the trees the taller one had blown down.

9. The car a sports car was parked in the street near our house.

Challenge

Think of a sensible way to finish each of these sentences.

1. During the heavy rainstorm, _____

2. Because it was my birthday, _____

3. Even though I didn't feel like it, _____

4. Last of all, _____

5. A long time ago, before I was born, _____

6. A lady, the one with the dark hair, _____

7. My dog, my lovely old dog, _____

8. The car, an old banger, _____

Word order

Look and learn

The man fried an egg.
The egg fried a man.

On Saturday I went shopping.
I went shopping on Saturday.

Sometimes when we **change the order of the words**, it **changes the meaning** of the sentence.	Sometimes we can change the order of the words and **not** change the meaning of the sentence.

Practice

Rearrange these words to make sensible sentences.

1. moo. Cows can   Cows can moo.
2. dog bones. My likes   _____
3. fast. grey The runs horse   _____
4. football. Yesterday played boy the   _____
5. a The crashed into car wall.   _____
6. workmen tea. drinking Some were   _____
7. by town went We to bus.   _____
8. noise. Bees a buzzing make   _____
9. webs. their Spiders insects catch in   _____
10. a long A tail. has mouse   _____

Challenge

Change some words round. Make some silly sentences of your own.

1. The builder fell off the ladder.   _____
2. A lady was watching the television.   _____
3. The boy mowed the lawn.   _____
4. Some children ate some crisps.   _____
5. The singer played the guitar.   _____
6. The clown wore some baggy trousers.   _____
7. The teacher is reading a book.   _____
8. The postman delivered a parcel.   _____

Apostrophes marking possession

Look and learn

We use an **apostrophe** to show **ownership** (that something belongs to someone).

The girl's pens

The girls' pens

When there is only **one** owner, we usually write **'s**.

When there is **more** than one owner, we usually write **s'**.

Practice

Write the shortened form of each phrase.

1. _____the golfer's clubs_____ the clubs belong to the golfer
2. _____ the hammer belongs to the builder
3. _____ the boots belong to the footballer
4. _____ the branches of the tree
5. _____ the pen belongs to my uncle
6. _____ the book belongs to my sister
7. _____ the tractor belongs to the farmer
8. _____ the glasses belong to Karen
9. _____ the slippers belong to Mr Smith
10. _____ the tail of the dinosaur

Challenge

Write what each of these phrase means.

1. the elephant's trunk _____the trunk of the elephant_____
2. the elephants' ears _____
3. the sailors' ship _____
4. the ants' nest _____
5. the bird's eggs _____
6. the boys' books _____
7. the boys' bags _____
8. the teachers' room _____
9. the dogs' owner _____
10. the cat's eyes _____

Compound words

Look and learn

A **compound** word is made up of **two smaller words** joined together.

butter   +   fly   =   butterfly

Practice

Match up the words to make some compound words.

1. after	fast	_____
2. birth	sight	_____
3. break	way	_____
4. cloak	noon →	afternoon
5. cup	step	_____
6. eye	room	_____
7. foot	card	_____
8. post	come	_____
9. motor	day	_____
10. over	board	_____

Challenge

Think of a word to go at the beginning or end of these words to make some more compound words.

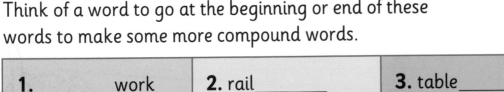

1. _____work	2. rail_____	3. table_____
4. _____bow	5. round_____	6. _____paper
7. _____fall	8. when_____	9. some_____
10. _____brush	11. hand_____	12. _____hole

22

Diminutives

Look and learn

Diminutives are words that imply something **small**.

duck – duckling

sheep – lamb

A **diminutive** can sometimes be made by adding a **suffix**.	A **diminutive** can sometimes be a **different word altogether**.

Practice

Choose the correct diminutive for each animal.

calf	fawn	cub	chick	puppy
lamb	kitten	foal	kid	leveret

1. horse ___foal___ 2. sheep _____

3. cat _____ 4. dog _____

5. bear _____ 6. goat _____

7. hen _____ 8. deer _____

9. hare _____ 10. cow _____

Challenge

Give each diminutive its correct suffix. Say what each thing is.

1. gos<u>ling</u>_____ (ling/en)   ___A gosling is a small goose.___

2. eag_____ (ling/let) _____

3. owl_____ (let/en) _____

4. hill_____ (kin/ock) _____

5. kitchen_____ (ock/ette) _____

6. maid_____ (ette/en) _____

7. duck_____ (ling/let) _____

8. book_____ (let/ling) _____

9. lamb_____ (en/kin) _____

10. statu_____ (ette/kin) _____

Surprising sounds

Look and learn

Letters don't always sound the way we expect them to!

watch

warm

work

| Listen to the sound of **a** when it comes after **w**. | Listen to the sound of **ar** when it comes after **w**. | Listen to the sound of **or** when it comes after **w**. |

Practice

Choose the correct word to complete each sentence.

1. The early bird catches the _____worm_____.
2. At school we have to _____ hard.
3. There are many different countries in our _____.
4. When the sun shines it is _____.
5. The vase was _____ a lot of money.
6. Most parents _____ their children about busy roads.
7. The _____ of bees left their hive.
8. My spelling seems to get _____ rather than better.
9. If you catch a thief you may get a _____.
10. The police had a _____ for the burglar's arrest.

war	wor
warm	world
warn	worth
warrant	worse
swarm	worm
reward	work

Challenge

Make these words. Circle the odd one out in each set.

1.
c
b
d — ash
w
cr
cash
_____
_____
_____
_____

2.
w
b
gr — and
st
l
_____
_____
_____
_____
_____

3.
g
gr
w — ander
p
me
_____
_____
_____
_____
_____

4.
b
w
m — atch
h
l
_____
_____
_____
_____
_____

Types of sentences

Look and learn

There are **four** different **types of sentences**.

A **statement** gives **information**.

My car is red.

A **question asks** something.

Does it go fast?

A **command tells** someone to do something.

Get in.

An **exclamation** shows someone **feels something strongly**.

It's great!

Practice

Which type of sentence is each of these?

1. The door is open.
2. Have you seen my shorts?
3. What a lovely surprise!
4. Go and have a wash.
5. Where is Carla?
6. It was terrible!
7. I'm going out to play.
8. Keep quiet!
9. How old are you?
10. Come with me.

statement	question	command	exclamation
✓			

Challenge

Write these sentences and punctuate them correctly. After each sentence, write if it is a **statement** (S), **a question** (Q), **a command** (C) or **an exclamation** (E).

1. how far is it to the united states of america

_____ ( )

2. bring me my hat coat gloves and bag Philip

_____ ( )

3. im going to france for my holiday

_____ ( )

4. help theres a monster chasing me

_____ ( )

Experimenting with words

Look and learn

We can add **suffixes** to **some** types of words but not others.

look – looking – looked

We **can** add suffixes to **verbs**.

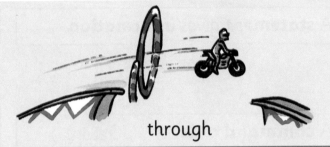

through

We **can't** add suffixes to **prepositions**.

Practice

Complete this chart.

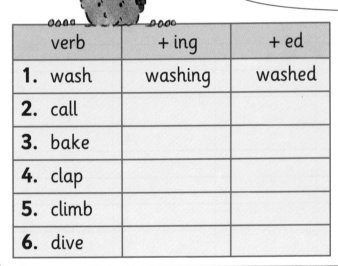

Take care! Sometimes you may have to change the spelling of the root verb.

verb	+ ing	+ ed
1. wash	washing	washed
2. call		
3. bake		
4. clap		
5. climb		
6. dive		

verb	+ ing	+ ed
7. open		
8. joke		
9. nod		
10. breathe		
11. refuse		
12. tug		

Challenge

Write whether each word is a **verb** (V) or **preposition** (P).

Try adding the suffix **ing** to each word to find out!

1. break (V)   2. behind ( )

3. into ( )   4. see ( )

5. over ( )   6. show ( )

7. think ( )   8. up ( )

9. towards ( )   10. from ( )

11. under ( )   12. teach ( )

The word endings tion or sion

Look and learn

The two common word endings **tion** and **sion** sometimes get confused.

conversation

television

| The **tion** at the end of words sounds like **shun**. | The **sion** at the end of words sounds like **zhon**. |

Practice

Write the noun that comes from each of these verbs.

tion	sion
examination	explosion
competition	decision
decoration	invasion
action	erosion
creation	confusion
preparation	division

1. invade _invasion_

2. decorate _____

3. prepare _____

4. confuse _____

5. explode _____

6. divide _____

7. examine _____

8. create _____

9. compete _____

10. decide _____

11. erode _____

12. act _____

Challenge

Mark this spelling test.

1. conclution ☒
2. information ☐
3. destrucsion ☐
4. revision ☐
5. inclusion ☐
6. generasion ☐
7. population ☐
8. sensasion ☐
9. composition ☐
10. incision ☐
11. propostition ☐
12. fracsion ☐

Write some words ending in **ssion**.

possession
_____
_____
_____

The word endings able or ible

Look and learn

The two common word endings, **able** and **ible**, often get confused.

fashion + able = fashionable

It is often possible to see the root word when **able** is added.

horror + ible = horrible

It is **not** often possible to see the root word when **ible** is added.

Practice

Choose the best word to complete each sentence.

1. At home I am __responsible__ for doing the washing up.
2. The archaeologist made a _____ discovery.
3. I like to wear _____ clothes.
4. My favourite armchair is very _____.
5. I made a _____ mistake.
6. It is _____ to win the lottery – but not likely!
7. When something disappears it is _____.
8. When I am sad I feel quite _____.
9. It is not _____ to run across the road.
10. The opposite of unreasonable is _____.

able	ible
comfortable	possible
reasonable	terrible
fashionable	responsible
remarkable	sensible
miserable	invisible

Challenge

Choose **able** or **ible** to complete each word.

1. flex_____ible_____
2. understand_____

3. laugh_____
4. incred_____

5. aud_____
6. agree_____

7. punish_____
8. obtain_____

9. favour_____
10. indel_____

11. divis_____
12. change_____

Common letter strings

Look and learn

Some **letter strings** are very **common** – but they do not always make the same sound!

cough

tough

bough

thr**ough**

Practice

Write the pairs of words which contain the same letter strings.

trough	grow
post	shoulder
allow	look
hour	gone
could	give
one	though
bear	have
five	hear
soon	cost
wave	pour

1. _____
2. _____
3. _____
4. _____
5. _____
6. _____trough_____though_____
7. _____
8. _____
9. _____
10. _____

Challenge

Make up some sentences. Use each pair of words in a sentence.

1. moth   mother   ___**Mother** caught the **moth** in the net.___
2. office   mice   _____
3. glove   move   _____
4. die   believe   _____
5. snow   cow   _____
6. case   vase   _____
7. line   machine   _____
8. wallet   mallet   _____

Conjunctions

Look and learn

A **conjunction** is a joining word. It may be used to join **two sentences**.

It was raining. I put up my umbrella.
(two sentences)

It was raining **so** I put up my umbrella.
(one sentence with a conjunction)

Practice

Make these pairs of sentences into one sentence.
Choose the best conjunction from the words in brackets.

1. The lion looked fierce. It was tame. (but/and/so)
   The lion looked fierce but it was tame.
2. I hurt my ankle. I fell off my bike. (and/so/when)
   _____
3. I went to bed early. I was tired. (whether/so/because)
   _____
4. It rained hard. I got soaked. (and/because/if)
   _____
5. Sharif did his spellings. He got them all right. (but/and/when)
   _____
6. The birds flew away. A cat was after them. (and/because/so)
   _____

Challenge

Think of a suitable ending for each sentence. Underline the conjunctions in each.

1. Sam's favourite food is pizza <u>but</u> _____
2. I went home when _____
3. I had to stay in so _____
4. It became very cold because _____
5. Alice put on her swimming costume and _____
6. Mr Patel turned off the television when _____
7. This is the naughty boy who _____
8. We ran across the bridge which _____

Positive and negative

Look and learn

 I liked the film.

 I didn't like the film.

This is a **positive** sentence. It means **yes**.

This is a **negative** sentence. It means **no**. The main negative is **not** or **n't**.

Practice

Say whether each sentence is positive (✓) or negative (✗).

1. I love snakes.   ✓
2. I don't like spelling. _____
3. We are not allowed to stay up late. _____
4. Chantel is good at climbing. _____
5. This is the best ice cream ever. _____
6. New York is not in Canada. _____
7. Poor Sarah is not very well. _____
8. I can't say the alphabet backwards. _____
9. I hate sprouts. _____
10. My favourite hobby is collecting stamps. _____

Challenge

Write each of these negative sentences and make each one positive.

1. Elizabeth is not a girl. _____ Elizabeth is a girl. _____
2. Don't wear your old clothes. _____
3. You are not allowed to swim here. _____
4. It is not very fair. _____
5. Justin can't play the piano. _____
6. It is not raining today. _____
7. Shirley was not able to do the sum. _____
8. You shouldn't wave at me. _____
9. The sea wasn't very warm. _____
10. Hedgehogs don't have prickly spines. _____

Answers

Page 2
Practice: 1. invented, 2. dried, 3. learn, 4. are, 5. is, 6. jumped, 7. left, 8. picked, 9. dug, 10. yapped
Challenge: answers may vary

Page 3
Practice: 2. holiday, 3. window, 4. throw, 5. push, 6. point, 7. howl, 8. claw, 9. saucer, 10. loud, 11. food, 12. enjoy
Challenge: answers may vary

Page 4
Practice:
past: 2. drank, 4. crossed, 6.broke down, 7. gave
present: 3. is riding, 9. am eating, 10. likes
future: 5. will go, 8. will sleep
Challenge:
2. I will play with my friend.
3. We will ride our bikes to school.
4. In the morning we will do Maths.
5. For lunch I will have pizza.
6. In the afternoon I will paint a picture.
7. I will go to the shop after school.
8. In the evening I will watch TV.

Page 5
Practice: 2. window, 3. magnet, 4. unlock, 5. inside, 6. sister, 7. spider, 8. tiger, 9. robot, 10. label, 11. hero, 12. pupil
Challenge: 2. lantern, 3. trumpet, 4. invent, 5. kidnap, 6. silent, 7. student, 8. teacher, 9. doctor, 10. princess

Page 6
Practice: 2. singer, 3. baker, 4. gardener, 5. boxer, 6. skater, 7. reporter, 8. cleaner, 9. dancer, 10. drummer, 11. driver, 12. swimmer
Challenge: 2. actor, 3. inspector, 4. printer, 5. voter, 6. visitor, 7. professor, 8. editor, 9. glider, 10. sailor

Page 7
Practice:
1. slap/sleep/slip
2. flame/flick/flock
3. pray/prepare/prod
4. sharp/shoulder/shut
5. drag/drop/drum/dry
6. beak/bee/beg/bell
7. coat/code/cork/cost
8. chatter/cheese/chip/chop
9. baby/badge/balloon/base
10. pear/pebble/pest/pet
Challenge:
1. beast/beaten/beaver
2. canal/candle/cannon
3. comic/command/computer
4. helicopter/hello/helping
5. scrap/scroll/scrub
6. strength/stride/stroke
(some answers may vary)

Page 8
Practice: tide/tied, ball/bawl, heard/herd, bare/bear, here/hear, faint/feint, their/there, find/fined, berth/birth, hair/hare, draft/draught, flour/flower, check/cheque, steal/steel, fir/fur
Challenge: Last week I thought I would go for a sail on the sea. I went down to the quay and made my way to the boat. The tide was right in.

Page 9
Practice: 2. fell (verb) heavily (adverb), 3. spoke (verb) rudely (adverb), 4. smiled (verb) sweetly (adverb), 5. smacked (verb) noisily (adverb), 6. cross (verb) carefully (adverb), 7. wrote (verb) neatly (adverb), 8. angrily (adverb) kicked (verb), 9. growled (verb) fiercely (adverb), 10. shone (verb) brightly (adverb)
Challenge: 2. bravely/fearlessly, 3. shyly/timidly, 4. happily/cheerfully, 5. distinctly/clearly, 6. sadly/unhappily, 7. badly/poorly, 8. slowly/sluggishly, 9. noisily/boisterously, 10. carefully/cautiously

Page 10
Practice: 1. island, 2. business, 3. friend, 4. separate, 5. brother, 6. heard, 7. hospital, 8. every, 9. want, 10. breakfast
Challenge: 2. knowledge, 3. lightning, 4. present, 5. sandwich, 6. sword, 7. vegetable, 8. weather, 9. weight, 10. whole (some answers may vary)

Page 11
Practice: 2. slowly, 3. proudly, 4. hungrily, 5. lazily, 6. merrily, 7. easily, 8. simply, 9. humbly, 10. horribly
Challenge: 2. grateful, 3. weary, 4. idle, 5. miserable, 6. skilful, 7. brave, 8. steady, 9. lucky, 10. noisy, 11. sudden, 12. true

Page 12
Practice: 2. muddy, 3. heavy, 4. blunt, 5. nasty, 6. slippery, 7. sad, 8. loud, 9. choppy, 10. howling
Challenge: answers may vary

Page 13
Practice: 2. sweet, 3. smooth, 4. light, 5. soft, 6. flat, 7. gentle, 8. red, 9. cool, 10. heavy, 11. slow, 12. strong
Challenge: answers may vary

Page 14
Practice: 2. might, 3. night, 4. right, 5. sight, 6. fudge, 7. badge, 8. dodge, 9. bridge, 10. hedge, 11. more, 12. core, 13. bore, 14. sore, 15. tore
Challenge: 2. government, 3. station, 4. enough, 5. clear, 6. blood, 7. spire, 8. insure, 9. catch, 10. appearance

Page 15
Practice: 1. lightest, 2. faster, 3. round/roundest, 4. softer/softest, 5. long/longer, 6. cold/coldest, 7. smoother/smoothest, 8. slow/slower, 9. sharp/sharpest, 10. rougher/roughest
Challenge: 2. larger/largest, 3. tamer/tamest, 4. hotter/hottest, 5. thinner/thinnest, 6. sadder/saddest, 7. heavier/heaviest, 8. luckier/luckiest, 9. uglier/ugliest 10. prettier/prettiest

Page 16
Practice: 2. comic/comical, 3. magic/magical, 4. person/personal, 5. coast/coastal, 6. accident/accidental, 7. season/seasonal, 8. origin/original, 9. topic/topical, 10. mechanic/mechanical
Challenge: 2. athletic, 3. customary, 4. illness, 5. childhood, 6. leadership, 7. darken, 8. punctuate, 9. horrify, 10. magnetise

Page 17
Practice:
masculine: boy/uncle/husband/king/nephew
feminine: queen/girl/aunt/wife/niece
common: pupil/friend/teacher/doctor/child
Challenge:
2. The queen looked at the princess.
3. The woman told her daughter off.
4. My sister is going to be a policewoman.
5. Lady Jones spoke to Mrs Derby.

Page 18
Practice: 2. was not, 3. can not, 4. do not, 5. did not, 6. it is, 7. you are, 8. I am, 9. we will, 10. they have, 11. will not, 12. she is
Challenge:
2. You've got a lovely hairstyle.
3. The dog doesn't have a lead.
4. He's cheating.
5. We'll do it later.
6. I didn't know what to do.
7. They're his shorts.
8. I'd rather do it myself.

Page 19
Practice:
1. Put on your coat, Emma.
2. Sorry, miss.
3. We'll go now, shall we?
4. No, don't do that!
5. The rabbit, a white fluffy animal, escaped from its cage.
6. I saw two children, Sam and Peter, in the shop.
7. To my surprise, the children did not recognise me.
8. One of the trees, the taller one, had blown down.
9. The car, a sports car, was parked in the street, near our house.
Challenge: answers may vary